PUFFIN BOOKS

Five Facts About Tony Bradman

1. He's written loads of children's books, all of which are completely brilliant.

2. He's got three children and one grandchild (even though he doesn't look nearly old enough to be a grandfather).

3. He used to be a music journalist (cool!).

4. The kinds of lists he doesn't like are: shopping lists and lists of things to do like 'Pay the gas bill' and 'Clean the bathroom'.

5. The kinds of lists he likes are: his birthday-present list, his Christmas-present list and VERY SILLY LISTS.

Tony Bradman

Very Silly Lists

Illustrated by Ian Cunliffe

PUFFIN BOOKS

PUFFIN BOOKS

Published by the Penguin Group
Penguin Books Ltd, 80 Strand, London WC2R 0RL, England
Penguin Putnam Inc., 375 Hudson Street, New York, New York 10014, USA
Penguin Books Australia Ltd, Ringwood, Victoria, Australia
Penguin Books Canada Ltd, 10 Alcorn Avenue, Toronto, Ontario, Canada M4V 3B2
Penguin Books India (P) Ltd, 11 Community Centre, Panchsheel Park, New Delhi – 110 017, India
Penguin Books (NZ) Ltd, Cnr Rosedale and Airborne Roads, Albany, Auckland, New Zealand
Penguin Books (South Africa) (Pty) Ltd, 5 Watkins Street, Denver Ext 4, Johannesburg 2094, South Africa

Penguin Books Ltd, Registered Offices: 80 Strand, London WC2R 0RL, England

www.penguin.com

First published 2000
4

Made and printed in England by Clays Ltd, St Ives plc

British Library Cataloguing in Publication Data
A CIP catalogue record for this book is available from the British Library

ISBN 0–141–30690–4

CONTENTS

HOLIDAYS
Sun, sea and ... more silly lists!

THE VERY SILLIEST LISTS OF ALL
A ridiculous collection of lists that
wouldn't fit anywhere else!

A word from the author ...

I was just sitting doing nothing one afternoon (which isn't unusual for a writer) when the phone rang. It was a nice editor (well, I thought she was nice at the time) asking if I wanted to write something called *Very Silly Lists*. I said I was too busy and had a list of things to do as long as ... well, as long as a very long list. In fact, I was so busy, I had several different lists of things to do and was thinking about making a list of all my lists so I'd know what was on each of them.

Anyway, we talked for a bit and I agreed to put the idea on my list of 'Things to Think About'. When I'd thought about it, I made a list of reasons to do it, reasons not to do it, and a list of things I'd rather be doing instead, and then suddenly, the lists started to get VERY SILLY and I just couldn't stop.

So here it is, a book of the silliest lists you've ever seen. I hope you like them. If you don't ...

well, just make a list of the reasons why, and keep it to yourself.

Yours,

Otherwise known as:

1. Anthony John Bradman (my full name).
2. Tone.
3. Dad.
4. Grandpop.
5. Bradders (my school nickname).
6. Stumpy (my other school nickname).

P.S. The author would like to stress that no hamsters, rhinoceroses, brothers, sisters or teachers were harmed in the making of this book.

(Can we get on with it now? The Editor.)

Ten Things Your Teacher Could Do to Really Impress the Class

1. Peel off his/her rubber face-mask to reveal a hideous alien underneath.

2. Burp louder than anybody else in the entire class.

3. Be outrageously cheeky to the head.

4. Do a backwards flip into the classroom – no hands.

5. Announce that he/she is giving up teaching for an easier and less stressful job, e.g. lion-taming.

6. Hand out bundles of £50 notes to everyone in the class.

7. Ask you what he/she should write in your reports.

8. Remember everybody's names all year round and not get them wrong once.

9. Come to school by private jet.

10. Saw one of the other teachers in half.

Ten Things You Wouldn't Like for School Dinners

1. Rancid Mongolian yak-manure cakes.
2. A six-and-a-half-year-old hamburger.
3. Boiled underpants.
4. Worm spaghetti.
5. An omelette made from six-thousand-year-old Chinese eggs.
6. A meat pie made from your pet hamster.
7. Cat-food rissoles.
8. A hot dog made from a real dog.
9. Slugs on toast (with a side order of dog poo).
10. Rotting sheeps' eyeballs in dog vomit (although several schools feature this dish under another name).

Ten Things You Wouldn't Normally Expect to Find in Your School Desk or Locker

1. A double-decker bus.
2. A black hole leading to a number of parallel universes.
3. Your auntie Mavis.
4. The missing crew of the *Marie Celeste*.
5. A lifetime's supply of hamburgers.
6. Elvis Presley.

7. Every sock that's ever been lost since the beginning of recorded time.
8. A herd of elephants.
9. The planet Mars.
10. A number of exercise books, with lots of good, neat work in them that's been given top marks by your admiring teacher.

Ten Things Teachers Do When They're Not at School

1. Plan the most boring lessons they can.
2. Make little dolls resembling their head teacher and stick pins in them.

3. Eat all the sweets they've confiscated from their pupils.
4. Dream about becoming Dictator of the Entire Universe.
5. Practise writing sarcastic comments on schoolwork, reports, etc.
6. Phone up other teachers and swop tips on how to make their lessons even more boring.
7. Wish they were children again and could run round the playground having a good time, being really cheeky to all the teachers, etc.
8. Go to top secret government training-centres where they're taught how to make their pupils' lives as miserable as possible.
9. Fill out job applications for any job not involving teaching or kids.
10. Think about going to work the next day, cry a lot, tear their hair out, etc.

Ten Subjects You'd Love to Study at School

1. The art of chocolate-bar eating.

2. Advanced cheek, with special reference to giving lip to parents and teachers and getting away with it.

3. Television, particularly soaps, music shows, and the kind of inappropriate, grown-up films your parents don't usually let you watch.

4. Advanced methods and techniques for pocket-money extraction.

5. Brilliant tricks and stunts to perform in the playground that will convince your friends you're a total superstar.

6. How to stay awake in maths lessons.

7. How to doze off during parental or teacher lectures about bad behaviour, laziness, strangling your little brother/sister, etc, and yet still appear to be wide awake, and listening.

8. Advanced techniques for persuading your parents to buy you whatever you want (ie, hypnotism).

9. Really obscure computer-game cheats that will astound and amaze your friends.

10. How to remember and tell loads of utterly brilliant jokes.

Ten Words Nobody Can Spell, Not Even Teachers, and That Would Guarantee You a World-record Score in Scrabble if You Could Use Any of Them

1. Zygobranchiate.
2. Isobathytherm.
3. Floccinaucinihilipilification.
4. Haemodynamometer.
5. Dephlogisticate.
6. Ichthyodorylite.
7. Tintinnabulation.
8. Syncotyledonous.
9. Rhyncocephalian.
10. Diarrhoea.

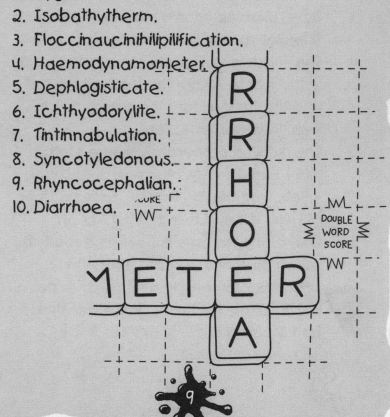

Ten Things That Always Happen During the School Nativity Play

1. Somebody drops the baby Jesus doll on its head during the big final scene.
2. Part of the scenery falls down, usually on some parents.
3. Several of the infants playing angels wet themselves and burst into tears.
4. The Three Wise Men do something stupid, ie get lost between the back of the hall and the front, forget the presents, trip over their costumes, etc.
5. The girl who desperately wanted to be Mary and didn't get the part spends the whole time making horrible faces at the girl who did and trying to put her off.
6. One of the parents annoys everybody by taking flash photographs every thirty seconds, clambering over seats to get a better angle for their camcorder shots, and shouting out – 'that's our Tracey – isn't she fantastic?'

7. The teacher playing the piano gets muddled up and plays the wrong music for each carol.
8. Somebody's grandad falls asleep in the front row, snores loudly, then wakes up suddenly in the middle of a crucial scene and starts clapping.
9. The boys playing the shepherds sing 'While shepherds washed their socks by night, all seated round the tub, the angel of the Lord came down and gave their smalls a scrub!' Then they burst into laughter and sit there smirking for the rest of the performance.
10. The head swears never to have another nativity play ever again, over his/her dead body, etc.

Ten People You Wouldn't Like to Have as a Teacher

1. Count Dracula.
2. Norman Nerdly, The World's Most Boring Human Being.
3. The Demon Headmaster.
4. Gordon, The Child-eating Giant with Very Bad Breath.
5. That Teacher You Had in Year Two Who Could Never Remember Your Name.
6. Zorko, The Incredibly Disgusting, Evil Galactic Overlord of the Andromedan Tetrarchy.
7. Godzilla.
8. That Dinner Lady Who Looks as if She Eats Razor Blades for Breakfast.
9. Thwacker Thwaite, The Teacher with the World's Greatest Collection of Canes and Peculiarly Painful Weapons of Pedagogic Punishment. (Don't panic – he's retired!)
10. Your mum.

Ten Things You Can't Say to a Teacher Without Getting into Really Big Trouble

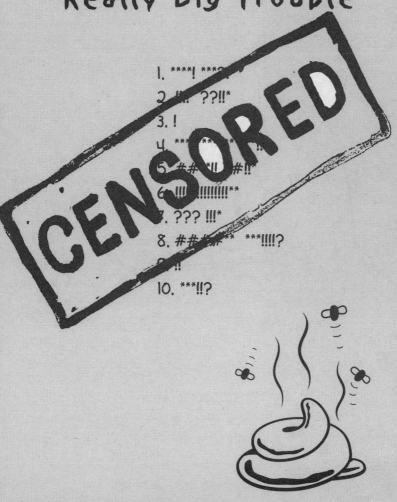

1. ****! ***?
2. !!! ??!!*
3. !
4. **** ** **!!
5. ##**!! #!!
6. !!! !!!!!!!! **
7. ??? !!!*
8. ##**!** ***!!!!?
9. !!
10. ***!!?

PETS

(WITH SPECIAL HAMSTER SECTION)

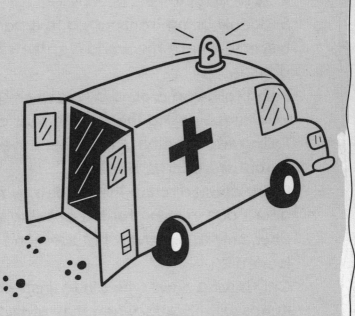

Ten Things Cats Don't Like Much

1. Being given an incredibly hard maths test without any time to prepare.
2. Not being fed the instant they decide they're hungry.
3. Suddenly being transported to a parallel universe where the world is entirely run by dogs.
4. Being followed around by a crawling baby who keeps poking them in the rear end.
5. Falling into a bath full of water, especially if it contains a large shark.
6. Being chased round the garden by next-door's dog, running for the cat flap in the door, only to discover that someone has locked it.
7. Only having paws with claws, instead of hands with fingers, when they really, really want to open the hamster's cage ...

8. Chasing a mouse which, when it's cornered, suddenly reveals that it is an alien in disguise, and turns itself into a giant, radioactive, savage killer beast, a thousand times more frightening than the creature in *Alien*.

9. Biting into something they think is a mouse's tail, only to discover that, in fact, it's a wire attached to a huge electricity pylon and carries a charge of twenty-five zillion volts.

10. Having their fur stroked the wrong way.

Ten Things Dogs Always Do

1. Make terrible smells while they're sleeping.
2. Drip disgusting doggy drool all over your new trainers.
3. Stare longingly at whatever you're eating.
4. Run into foul-smelling muddy puddles, then leap up and put their paws all over you and slobber at your face with their big, wet, smelly dog-breath tongues.
5. Sniff you in embarrassing places.
6. Get excited when you're playing football with your mates, bound over, bite the ball and burst it.
7. Stand in the middle of the front room, late at night, when you're watching a spooky film, growling at something they can see, but you can't ...
8. Sit by the back door whining to be let out into the garden, then thirty seconds later, start scratching and whining to be let in again.

9. Take an instant liking to the one person in your class you hate, friends of your parents that you can't stand, or elderly relatives you can't bear, who will now want to come back all the time because they like the dog so much.

10. Shed so much hair you find it in your clothes, your bed, your breakfast cereal ...

Ten Things You Can't Do with a Pet Goldfish

1. Take it for long walks in the country.
2. Teach it to fetch sticks.
3. Get it to say 'Who's a pretty goldfish then?'
4. Dress it up in doll's clothes and wheel it round the garden in a pram.
5. Teach it to play football.
6. Turn it into a courier goldfish and get it to take messages abroad.
7. Cuddle and stroke it while you watch TV (unless you flood the front room and wear a diving suit).
8. Get it to act as a guard fish and frighten off burglars.
9. Ride it in a gymkhana.
10. Ask it to help you with your homework.

Ten Things Tortoises Aren't Very Good at

1. The hundred-metre dash.
2. Being brain surgeons.
3. Aerobics.
4. Getting off their backs.
5. Rocket science.
6. Driving Formula One racing cars.
7. Being ballet dancers.
8. Getting into the Man. United first team.
9. Playing snap.
10. Winning beauty contests.

Ten Things Snakes Aren't Very Good at

1. Juggling.
2. Wearing shoes.
3. Doing hand signals when driving.
4. Knitting.
5. Standing on their heads.
6. Opening doors.
7. Flying an aeroplane.
8. Doing crossword puzzles.
9. Riding a bicycle.
10. Doing their times tables.

Ten Things Pet Rhinoceroses Aren't Very Good at

1. Making incredibly complicated scale-models of old ships, complete with rigging and sails, out of matchsticks.
2. Blowing their noses.
3. Staying concealed behind curtains during games of hide and seek.
4. Avoiding treading on your pet hamster while running around your bedroom.
5. Walking through a shop that sells incredibly delicate china, glass, etc, without breaking anything.
6. Fitting into the family car when you're all going on an outing.
7. Threading needles.
8. Hiding under your bed when they know they've done something wrong.
9. Getting through the cat flap.
10. Winning prizes for having extremely soft, beautiful skin.

Ten Reasons Why a Rhinoceros is a Better Pet Than a Hamster

1. With a rhinoceros, you've always got something to hang your hat on.
2. Cats very rarely frighten or attack rhinoceroses.
3. On show-and-tell days at school, not many of your friends will be able to bring in a pet as interesting and easy to keep as a rhinoceros.
4. Looking after a rhinoceros will help to make your whole family fitter, especially when you take him for walks in the park.
5. Rhinoceroses are very intelligent, and can be very affectionate.
6. A rhinoceros will help to protect your family from burglars.
7. Rhinoceros poo makes wonderful fertilizer for your mum and dad's garden. And for the gardens of everybody else

in your neighbourhood too.

8. A rhinoceros won't keep you awake half the night trundling around on a squeaky exercise wheel. Well, not too often anyway.

9. Saying to a school bully: 'If you don't leave me alone, I'll set my hamster on you,' isn't quite as effective as the same sentence with the words 'huge, unstoppable, savage killer rhinoceros' substituted for the word 'hamster'.

10. It just is.

SWAG

Ten Things Hamsters Are Not Very Good at

1. Being President of the USA.
2. Conversation.
3. Playing football for England. (Or for anyone, come to that.)
4. Living longer than a couple of years.
5. Rocket science.
6. Playing the piano.
7. Avoiding being half strangled by your little brother or sister who only wants 'to cuddle the ickle-sweetums hammy pie'.
8. Thinking of something original and interesting to do with an exercise wheel, a water bottle and a load of sawdust and wood chippings.
9. Snow-boarding.
10. Doing magic tricks.

Ten Undeniable, But Not Very Interesting Facts about Hamsters

1. A hamster has never won the Eurovision Song Contest.

2. No hamster has ever grown to the size of a whale.

3. Very few hamsters can whistle.

4. The word hamster does not appear in the Bible.

5. Hamsters have no sense of humour.

6. There were no hamsters on the *Apollo 11* mission to the moon.

7. Hamsters do not usually become best friends with cats, pythons or vultures.

8. No hamster has ever swum the Channel.

9. Hamsters do not generally walk on their hind legs while playing the trumpet.

10. If every hamster in the world were laid end to end, a lot of them would get trodden on, run over, eaten or drowned.

Ten Totally Stupid Names for a Pet Hamster

1. Rover.
2. Ickle-Sweetums-Darling-Lovey-Pops.
3. Killer.
4. Hamilton Heinrich Pothering Cholmondeley Featherstonehaugh Farnes-Barnes Junior III.
5. 43.
6. The Great Hairy Terrifying Savage Beast.
7. Michael Owen (unless your hamster is a good footballer and plays for Liverpool).
8. Tiddles.
9. Guy the Guinea Pig.
10. Hammy.

Ten Statements about Hamsters That Are Highly Unlikely

1. Hamsters are secretly the advance guard of an alien invasion force of super-intelligent rodents, dedicated to conquering Earth and putting us all in big cages, with giant exercise wheels, sawdust on the floor, etc.

2. Hamsters are the last remnants of the ancient civilization of Atlantis (capital city: Hamsteropolis), and they really built the Pyramids, the Great Wall of China, etc.

3. All hamsters can speak at least seventeen human languages. They're just shy.

4. Hamsters are the real reason the dinosaurs became extinct – they got fed up with being trampled on by those great big lizards and decided to sort them out once and for all.

5. Hamsters really adore being taken out of their cages, hugged very tightly, given big, dribbly kisses and listening to their owners say stuff like, 'Oo's a darling ickle-sweet lovey-pops hammy den?'

6. At night, hamsters secretly leave their cages and gather in secret hideouts where they have wild parties, gamble, dance, etc, and return before you wake up and realize they've gone. Which explains why they spend most of the day looking exhausted and dozing.

7. All hamsters can fly, but they just don't like showing off.

8. The Internet is secretly powered by hamsters who dash round the world delivering e-mails, so fast no one can see them doing it.

9. Hamsters discovered fire, invented the wheel and nuclear power.

10. Hamsters make great pets.

The Ten Most Famous Hamsters of All Time

1. Attila the Hamster, Scourge of the Mongolian Rat Herds.
2. Hannibal The Hamster – Cereal Killer.
3. Harry Hamsterini, The Incredible Hamster Escapologist.
4. Hamstercea, Queen of the Rodent Iceni.
5. Sir Hamsterworth Hilary, First Hamster to Climb Mount Everest.
6. Hammy Armstrong, First Hamster on the Moon. ('This is one giant leap for man ... and an even bigger one for a hamster!')
7. King Hamster of Hamelot and the Hamsters of the Round Exercise Wheel.
8. Hamsterellen of Troy. ('The Whiskers That Launched a Thousand Chips'.)
9. Hamsterdonna, Queen of Rodent Pop.
10. William Hamsterspeare, Rodent Dramatist. (Author of *Hamsterlet, King Hamster, MacHamster, A Midsummer Night's Hamster,* etc.)

Ten Things to Do with a Dead Hamster (Other Than Burying It in the Garden)

1. Wrap it up and give it to your brother/sister for Christmas or their birthday, look surprised when they scream, and say it was fine when you got it from the shop.

2. Leave it in the cage and wait to see how long it takes your mum and dad to work out that it's dead (best in the winter, unless you always have your heating up high).

3. Pop it in the freezer in a bag marked: Best Before (insert date of hamster's demise).

4. Give it a Viking burial – the full monty, ie, build a little Viking ship, stick on bits of painted orange cardboard to make it look as though it's on fire, put the hamster in it, surrounded by hamster food-treats and favourite objects from the hamster's life. Fill the bath, and launch the little ship on the water. Leave it there for your mum to discover when she goes to run that long, relaxing bath she likes.

5. Have it stuffed and mounted and keep it on your desk.

6. Have it stuffed and mounted and give it to your granny for Christmas.

7. Have it stuffed and mounted and use it as a door stop.

8. Donate its little body to veterinary science.

9. Have it stuffed and use it in a playground game of catch, rounders, football, etc.

10. Take it back to the shop where you got it, weep, complain bitterly, and ask for your money back or a new hamster.

Ten Classic Hamster Movies

1. *Paw Wars.*
2. *Paw Wars: The Hamster Strikes Back.*
3. *Paw Wars: The Return of the Hamster.*
4. *Paw Wars: The Phantom Hamster.*
5. *The Hamsternator.*
6. *Hamsterzilla.*
7. *Aliens versus Hamsters: The Final Conflict.*
8. *Jurassic Hamster.*
9. *Die Hamster (1, 2, 3, 4).*
10. *Saturday Night Hamster.*

Ten Reasons Why a Small Stone Makes a Terrific Pet

1. You never have to take it for walks in the pouring rain, snow, blizzards, etc.
2. It won't cost you anything in vet's bills. Well, not much anyway.
3. It won't make disgusting smells while you're cuddling it.
4. You won't find it dead in its cage one morning.
5. It won't suddenly give birth to fifteen baby stones.
6. Your mum won't be able to say it smells (unless you drop it in dog poo by accident).
7. It won't chase next-door's cat every time it sees it.
8. You can use it as a paperweight when you're doing your homework outside in high winds.
9. Unlike a hamster, it will be very useful for cracking nuts, banging in nails, etc.
10. If you get fed up with it, you can just throw it away (although be careful where you're aiming).

Ten Unusual
(and Disgusting)
Fast Foods

1. Rat in a Roll.
2. Rancid – The Yucky Yak-yogurt Drink.
3. Hamsterburger.
4. Budgie in a Bap.
5. Pot Poodle.
6. Snake and Vinegar Crisps.
7. Gerbil Jam Butties.
8. Chocolate Chip Chihuahuas.
9. Terrapin Toasties.
10. Kitten Kebabs.

Ten Things You Would Eventually Have to Eat If You Were Locked in the House with No Food

1. Face-flannel and toothpaste sandwiches.
2. Your shoes.
3. A hard bit of old chewing gum you stuck under the table two years ago.
4. Your dad's toenail clippings.
5. Scrapings from the dog's bowl.
6. Your brother or sister.
7. The giant inflatable plastic banana you bought on holiday last year to jump on in the swimming pool.
8. Your homework (well, it's better than saying the dog ate it).
9. Your left leg.
10. Your hamster.

Ten Incredibly Disgusting Sandwich Fillings

1. Cat food, cucumber and corn plasters.
2. Bacon, lettuce and old scabs.
3. Your mum's old tights, with horseradish and greenies.
4. Cheese and chutney, with a sprinkling of teacher dandruff.
5. Sewage sludge paste (must be on white bread to get full effect).
6. Hamster and onion, with maggoty lettuce on blackhead bread.
7. Five poo pâté (Dog, Hamster, Elephant, Rhinoceros, Baby).
8. Egg and dog vomit with watercress.
9. Curried chicken gizzard with sweet and sour rats' eyeballs.
10. Fish paste from an ancient jar your granny found at the back of one of her kitchen cupboards.

Ten Utterly Disgusting Crisp Flavours

1. Sneeze and Onion.
2. Salt and Greeny.
3. Snail Cocktail.
4. Dog Drool and Vinegar.
5. Smoky Hedgehog.
6. Curried Hamster.
7. Garlic and Old Socks.
8. Beef and Bogies.
9. Cheese and Vomit.
10. Ready Snotted.

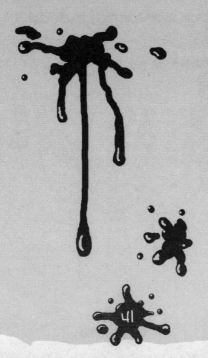

Ten Utterly Disgusting Things

1. A large jar full of toe jam.
2. A sculpture of your teacher made entirely out of your best friend's earwax.
3. A lolly made of sleepy dust.
4. A dog poo hot dog.
5. Seventeen pieces of grimy, slimy soap – covered in hairs and all stuck together.
6. A baby-sick milkshake.
7. A swimming pool full of diarrhoea.
8. An Everest-sized mountain made of huge, wet greenies.
9. A lunchbox containing a dead, mouldy hamster.
10. Your brother or sister.

Ten Totally Disgusting Things You Wouldn't Like to Be Given to Drink

1. A rancid yak-butter milkshake, with added bat droppings.
2. A cocktail of sewage sludge and radioactive water from a dodgy nuclear power station.
3. Warm, flat cola.
4. A cup of sick provided by your baby brother or sister.
5. Cocoa.
6. That nasty, smelly, brown liquid that always seems to be sloshing around in the bottom of your family's dustbin.
7. Any liquid supplied along with your school dinners.
8. The oil that drips out of the bottom of your dad's old banger.
9. Two gallons of spit provided by your classmates.
10. A cup of hot, sweet, milky tea made by your granny.

Ten Things You Wouldn't Want to Find in Your Dinner

1. Seventeen large white, wriggly maggots.
2. Half a human finger.
3. Enormous amounts of an especially toxic poison put there by your brother or sister.
4. An extremely large, wet, steaming greeny that didn't come from you ...
5. A note from your mum saying 'This is the dinner you refused to eat six months ago and you're not allowed to watch TV for ten years unless you eat it all up right now.'
6. A savage mutant killer-potato that eats all human beings.
7. Gravy made out of a combination of dog diarrhoea and yak vomit.
8. A sausage giving off a strange radioactive glow.
9. A dead, mouldy, rotting hamster.
10. Anything your mum says is good for you.

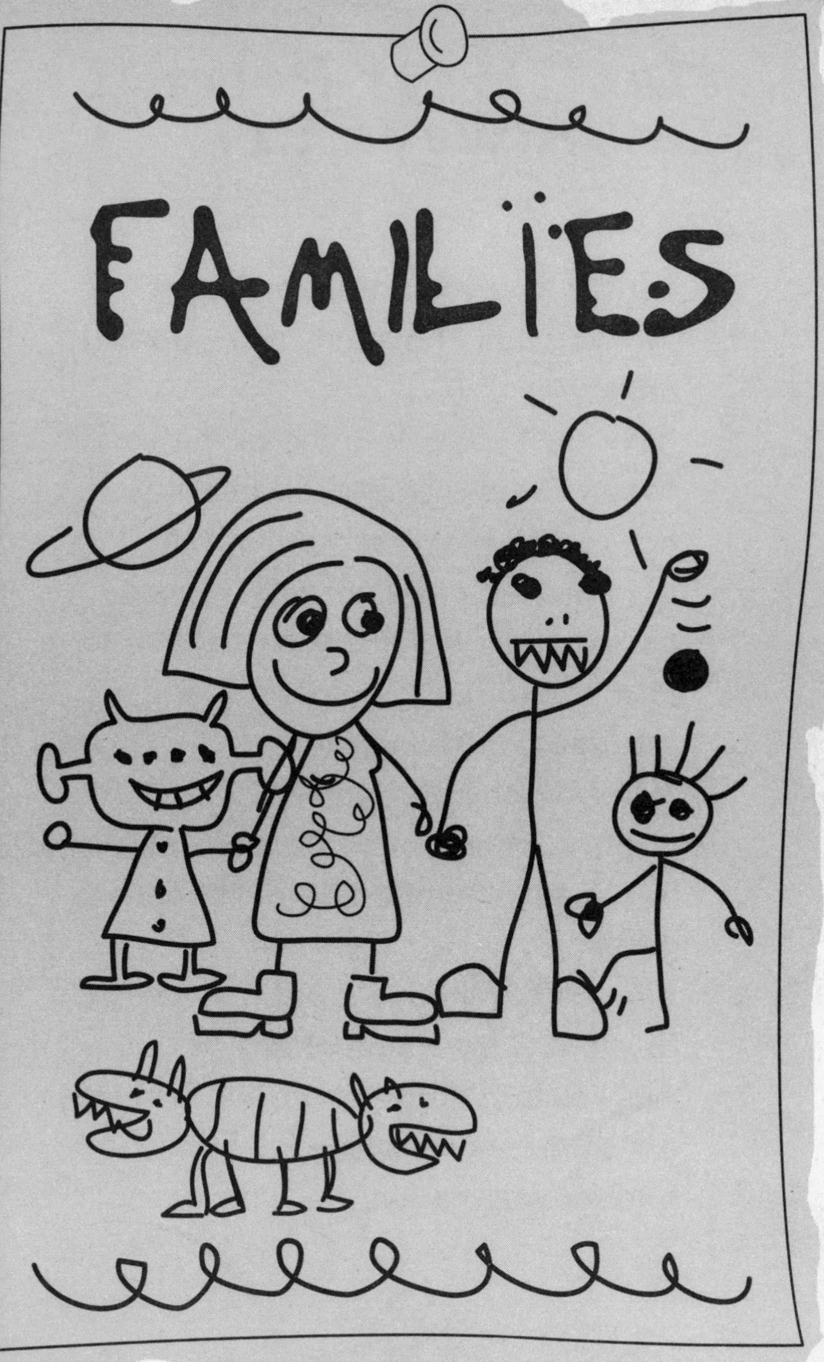
FAMILIES

Ten Things Parents Always Say

1. 'Isn't it time you tidied your room?'
2. 'No, you can't have any more pocket money.'
3. 'Why must you kids argue all the time?'
4. 'When I was your age, I would never have ...'(fill in appropriate activity disapproved of by parents, ie nose picking, door slamming, setting fire to Mum's apron).
5. 'No, you can't have the trainers/computer game/CD player/clothes you so desperately need because everyone else at school has got them.'
6. 'No, you can't have a pet. I'm allergic to ...' (fill in the name of any pet).
7. 'No, you can't have any chocolate/ice cream/fizzy drinks/junk food, they're bad for your health/teeth/brain, etc.'

8. 'How many times do I have to tell you not to ...' (fill in appropriate forbidden activity, ie, nose picking, strangling your little brother/sister, setting fire to Dad's slippers).

9. 'Yes, I am going to watch this gardening/cooking/home improvements programme, and you can't watch anything at all.'

10. 'Isn't it time you tidied your room again?'

Ten Things Parents Never Say.

1. 'How much pocket money should I give you?'

2. 'Of course we'll send your new baby brother back to the hospital where we got him.'

3. 'What you need is a week off school to watch eighteen-rated videos and eat huge amounts of junk food.'

4. 'If your room isn't untidy by the time I come back upstairs, you're in big trouble!'

5. 'I love it when you kids argue.'

6. 'No, of course you don't have to kiss your granny!'

7. 'When I was your age, I was cheeky, badly behaved, argued with my parents all the time and never did any work at school.'

8. 'No, of course I don't mind if you strangle your little sister.'

9. 'Yes, you can have a pet aardvark /black mamba/vulture/great white shark to keep in the bath. Why not have two?'

10. 'Why don't you have all your friends round for a wild sleepover party this weekend? We'd love to have the house wrecked and stay up all night!'

Ten Things That Always Happen at Christmas

1. Your little brother/sister opens all his/her presents at 2am, breaks most of them, then spends the rest of the day moaning, whining and crying, and is finally sick all over the sofa.

2. Your mum and dad have a row.

3. Ghastly relatives you thought (or hoped) were dead, turn up with awful, inappropriate presents, and expect to be thanked, kissed, etc.

4. Somebody forgets to get the turkey out of the freezer the night before, and your mum and dad spend the whole morning trying to ram it into the microwave and defrost it.

5. Your mum and dad have another row.

6. Your granny eats and drinks too much, goes on and on about the good old days in the sixties, takes her teeth out

50

to sing Beatles' songs, falls asleep, and snores so loudly no one can hear the TV.

7. The dog gets shut outside most of the day because he's been forgotten, and is so excited when he comes back in again that he pulls down the Christmas tree and widdles everywhere.

8. You're extremely disappointed with most of your presents and think that your brother/sister got much more than you, especially from your mum and dad.

9. You have a row with your brother/sister, and your mum and dad have another row as well.

10. Somebody says ... 'Only three-hundred-and-sixty-four days to go till next Christmas!'

Ten Ways to Completely Ruin Your Mum and Dad's Day

1. Tell them that your granny phoned while they were out, and that she said she was coming to stay for six months, maybe longer.

2. If they win the National Lottery, hide the ticket and tell them you've lost it. Better still, actually lose it.

3. Tell them that your teacher insists on them coming into school for special maths lessons four nights a week so they'll be able to understand the work you're doing.

4. Be especially nice to your brother or sister all day so that your mum and dad will think you're up to something and worry about what it is.

5. Completely re-paint every room in the entire house in yellow and pink stripes

while they're out and tell them it's part of a special art project you had to do.

6. Invite your entire class round for a special slap-up tea. If your mum and dad get cross, burst into tears and tell them nobody likes you and this is your only chance to make some friends.

7. Invite a friend round after school. After he or she has gone, tell your mum and dad that your friend has a small, deadly poisonous pet snake which he or she seems to have lost, and which was last seen slithering behind the sofa in the front room.

8. Give your mum and dad your next Christmas list – in January.

9. Spend the whole day walking on your hands and doing everything (eating meals, your homework, etc) with your feet.

10. Give them your school report.

Ten Excuses for Not Tidying Your Room

1. 'Who says it's untidy anyway?'
2. 'I like it this way – I know where everything is.'
3. 'Untidiness, dear parent, is in the eye of the beholder.'
4. 'My teacher says a little bit of untidiness is the sign of a creative mind. So I must be a total genius, and you should let me do what I like.'
5. 'I DO keep it tidy, but my pain of a brother/sister keeps sneaking in while I'm not here and untidying it.'
6. 'My brother/sister's room is much untidier than mine, and I don't hear you going on at him/her all the time ...'
7. 'If I tidy it, the poltergeist will only get angry and mess it all up again.'
8. 'There's no point in even TRYING to tidy my room. By the time I get it done, I'll have grown up and left home.'

54

9. 'I daren't tidy it. I'm too scared I'll find my missing hamster/loads of spiders/last term's packed lunches/Dad's smelly old socks under any pile I move.'

10. 'Tidy my room? Isn't that what parents are for?'

Ten Birthday Present Ideas for Your Brother/Sister

1. A gag.
2. A one-way ticket to the Andromeda Galaxy.
3. An exploding hamster.
4. Plastic surgery.
5. Deodorant.
6. A brain.
7. An outing to ... Count Dracula's castle.
8. A large, signed picture of yourself.
9. Two hundred tons of rhinoceros poo.
10. Something he or she has always wanted (as if!).

Ten Ways to Really Annoy Your Brother/Sister

1. Tell them over and over again that you really love them.
2. Forge a letter in your mum or dad's handwriting saying that YOU are their favourite, and they wish they'd never had your brother or sister, etc, then leave it where your brother or sister will find it.
3. Agree with absolutely everything he or she says.
4. Use your brother or sister's computer to hack into the Pentagon's defence computers, start World War III, then blame him/her.
5. Tell your granny that your brother or sister is desperate to come round after school every night and listen to lots of stories about how great it was in the good old days, the sixties, etc.
6. Follow him/her round all day long, whistling really tunelessly.

7. Tell everyone who phones for your brother/sister that he/she has moved out and is now living in Mongolia, but you don't have their phone number.

8. Scream hysterically every time he/she comes into the room, do a double-take, then say, 'Phew! It's you – for a second I thought it was a hideous monster ...'

9. Draw a moustache on every photograph of him/her that you can find in the house.

10. Keep telling your brother/sister everybody says he/she looks just like YOU.

Ten Things You'd Like to Do to Your Brother or Sister, But Probably Couldn't Get Away with

1. Waving a magic wand and turning him/her into a pig.

2. Making an interesting sculpture by super-gluing all his/her favourite CDs into an odd shape.

3. Turning his/her room completely upside down by gluing the furniture, carpet, etc, to the ceiling, just like in *The Twits*.

4. If Count Dracula appears in your room one night, directing him to your brother/sister's room and saying he/she has much more blood than you.

5. Persuading the aliens in a passing UFO to abduct him/her and return him/her strangely changed in a few years ...

6. Sell him/her to an experimental medical laboratory.

7. Give him/her a one-way ticket to Ulan Bator, capital of Mongolia, and make sure he/she actually gets on the train.

8. Bribe his/her teacher to give him/her the worst-ever school report in recorded history.

9. Invent a time machine and send him/her back to the Jurassic Era with a large sign on his/her back saying: 'Mmm! Yummy dinosaur snack available in one flavour only!'

10. Give him/her a pinch/kick/poke in the back while your mum and dad are watching.

SPORT

Ten Things You Probably Shouldn't Wear While Playing Football

1. Ice skates.
2. A big sign on your back saying, 'Please kick me, I love being fouled'.
3. A blindfold (although if you're a really useless player, this might not make much difference).
4. A Viking helmet and a pair of orange wellington boots.
5. That angel costume your mum made for your little sister when she was in the nativity play last Christmas.
6. Football boots made of chocolate.

7. Goggles, a snorkel, flippers and a swimming costume.
8. A suit of armour (unless of course you're playing The Penge District Girls Under-sevens, aka Crunchers FC, the dirtiest team in Britain).
9. A big sign on your front saying, 'The referee is always wrong.'
10. Shorts that are six sizes too small.

Ten People You Would Never See Playing Football for England

1. Darth Vader.
2. Winnie the Pooh.
3. Her Majesty the Queen.
4. That teacher you had in Year Four who coached the school football team, thought he was Michael Owen, but fell over every time he tried to kick the ball.
5. Cleopatra, Queen of the Nile.
6. Madonna.
7. Albert Einstein.
8. Pelé.
9. E.T.
10. Your Hundred-and-Four-Year-Old Great Auntie Nelly.

Ten Rules That Might Make Football More Interesting

1. The ball should be made of concrete.
2. Players should be accompanied on the pitch, at all times, by their mums.

3. Referees should only communicate with their players in Ancient Greek.

4. All pitches should be a maximum of two metres long and one metre wide.

5. Players should wear suits of armour, carry big swords, and ride horses.

6. Crowds at big matches should remain completely silent at all times.

7. All teams should only be allowed to have rhinoceroses as goalkeepers.

8. No team should have a manager who is more than three, or less than one-hundred-and-three years old.

9. In games played during the months of February, May and November, all players should be required to have their bootlaces tied together.

10. In all games between England and Germany, England should be given a twenty-five goal start.

Ten Very Silly New Rules That Would Make Cricket More Interesting (If Anything Could)

1. The ball should be a live hand-grenade.
2. The batsmen should be blindfolded and play in pairs with their legs tied together.
3. Wooden bats should be replaced by stuffed vampire bats.
4. Fielders should all be dressed as ballerinas, and a catch would only be allowed if the player making it was pirouetting at the time.
5. The area between the wickets should be mined.
6. All teams should play wearing roller skates and specially designed rocket packs on their backs.

7. Any team with more than six players whose surnames include the letter 'x', will be given a five-hundred run start.

8. All games should be played underwater.

9. Umpires should be allowed to have players executed for minor infringements of the rules.

10. The wickets should be replaced by goals at either end of a large rectangular pitch, bats should be dispensed with, the ball made bigger and both teams should try to kick or head it into the opposition's goal, the winning team being the one that scores the most goals in a period of ninety minutes, divided into two forty-five-minute halves. Or something like that anyway.

Ten Totally Stupid Athletic Events

1. The hundred-metre backwards-running sprint.
2. Blindfold javelin throwing.
3. Pole vault – without a pole.
4. The ten-metre marathon.
5. The hop, step and fall over.
6. The short jump.
7. Running head first into a brick wall.
8. The one-person relay race.
9. Throwing the dead hamster.
10. The four-hundred-metre three-legged hurdles.

Ten Great Imaginary Sporting Moments (That Will Probably Never Happen)

1. During an Olympic hundred-metre freestyle swimming final ... somebody pulls out the plug.

2. In the Grand National, all the horses suddenly screech to a halt and make the jockeys carry them round the course, over the jumps, etc.

3. For an Olympic sprint final, somebody secretly puts up a winning tape made out of extremely elastic rubber, so that when the runners hit it, they're catapulted back to the starting line.

4. During a Formula One Grand Prix, the cars come zooming round a bend only to discover a zebra crossing with a long line of old age pensioners, with shopping trolleys, slowly walking across it ...

5. A referee in a crucial football-championship awards a very dodgy penalty, and both sides, the crowd and the commentators in the TV studio all say that it was a very fair decision.

6. At the winter Olympics ski-jump final, one of the competitors takes off so fast he goes into orbit.

7. The Tour de France is won by a toddler on a tricycle.

8. At Wimbledon, a nervous player, facing someone with a very fast serve, comes out with a racquet ten metres across and hides behind it.

9. During an England versus Australia cricket match, both sides and the umpires suddenly realize that cricket is the most boring game in the universe, and go off to do something more interesting, such as play Monopoly, take up knitting or watch paint dry.

10. In the World Cup Final, England draw with Germany after extra time, then go on to win the penalty shoot-out.

HOLIDAYS

Ten Places You Probably Shouldn't Go on Holiday

1. Your local high street.
2. The bus stop at the end of your road.
3. An army firing range.
4. The central reservation of a motorway.
5. The council dump.
6. The rim of a large volcano that's about to explode.
7. The Arctic during a snow blizzard.
8. A swamp filled with alligators, poisonous snakes, leeches, radioactive waste, zombies, vampires and alien monsters.
9. Anywhere you think your teacher might go on holiday.
10. Anywhere with your family.

Ten Totally Useless Things to Take on Holiday

1. One flipper.
2. A tuba.
3. 'Burn-Aid – the cream that makes your skin super-sensitive to the sun!'
4. Your brother or sister.
5. A grand piano.
6. Two-hundred-and-forty-seven jars of out-of-date peanut butter.
7. Water wings made out of concrete (unless they're for your brother or sister).
8. A huge amount of extra school work you've promised to do for your teacher.
9. A supermarket shopping trolley.
10. A space suit.

Ten Things You Probably Shouldn't Wear While Swimming in the Sea

1. Concrete flippers.
2. A cream specially designed to attract sharks, particularly very big, very hungry ones.
3. Swimming shorts or a costume made from a material that explodes on contact with salt water.
4. Rollerblades.
5. A gorilla suit.
6. The smelly, mouldy, rotting swimming shorts or costume that you left in a plastic bag, while still damp, after your holiday a year ago.
7. A false shark outfit in an area where the locals shoot sharks on sight, or blow them up with massive depth charges.
8. Swimming shorts or a costume made from a material that dissolves on

contact with salt water.

9.	Swimming shorts or a costume made from a material that releases a huge cloud of luminous, bright-green dye that forms the letters, 'Look at me! I've just piddled in the water!' (as if you would ever do such a disgusting thing).

10.	A Darth Vader outfit.

Ten Things to Do if You Encounter a Ravenous Great White Shark While Swimming in the Sea

1. Say you'd like to stop and chat, but you have an important appointment on land.
2. Suddenly develop the ability to swim faster than a speeding motorboat.
3. Tell the shark that he's nothing but a great big bully and that you're just not scared of him.
4. Poke him in the eye with your finger. If that just makes him more angry, refer to (2) above.
5. Offer to race him to land, then laugh when he swims on to the beach and suddenly realizes he hasn't got any legs to walk on.
6. Tell him that if he tries anything, you'll get

your dad to beat him up. Or better still,
your mum. If that doesn't work, refer to
(2) above again.

7. Offer to introduce him to your brother
    or sister.

8. Distract him by talking about football
    until help arrives.

9. Tell him that your all-time favourite film is
    Jaws, and ask him for his autograph.

10. Panic, scream hysterically, thrash about
    in the water and get eaten.

Ten Things You Probably Shouldn't Do on an Aeroplane

1. Insist that you bring your pet rhinoceros on board with you.

2. Go to the toilet, and on the way back to your seat, say in a loud voice that you've just seen the pilot by one of the emergency exits, strapping on a parachute and praying.

3. Take a folded-up inflatable whale on board with you, ask if you can go and see the pilot flying the plane, then suddenly inflate the whale when you're on the control deck.

4. Play cricket in the aisles when the stewards and stewardesses are handing out the in-flight meal.

5. Actually eat the in-flight meal (and your brother/sister's as well).

6. Take a book called *Great Air Disasters* on board with you, and read from it in a loud voice throughout the flight.

7. Take a powerful laptop computer on board with you, hack into the plane's computers, take over from the pilot, and fly the plane as if you were playing a wild flight-simulation computer game.

8. Flood the control deck with a gas that makes the pilot, co-pilot and navigator behave in incredibly silly ways.

9. Saw a hole in the fuselage next to your seat to get a little more fresh air.

10. Sit next to your brother or sister.

Ten Games to Play in the Car on Long Boring Journeys

1. Count how many times you can say 'Are we nearly there yet?' before your mum and dad totally lose their tempers.

2. Play 'I Spy', but when it's your turn, don't have anything in mind, so that the game goes on and on until everyone gets really cross and starts arguing.

3. Have a secret bet with your brother or sister about how many times your mum will tell your dad (or vice versa) to slow down, watch the traffic ahead, drive more carefully, etc.

4. See how many times you can be sick on your brother or sister.

5. Challenge your brother/sister to a 'Who-can-hold-their-breath-the-longest' contest, then let them do it on their own.

6. Play Confessions and reveal a few

unimportant things you've done, then persuade your brother/sister to keep revealing more and more awful crimes, until finally he/she gets into really big trouble with your parents.

7. Agree with your brother or sister to keep absolutely silent and well-behaved during the entire journey and then take bets on how long it will be before your mum and dad stop the car to find out just what it is you're up to in the back ...

8. Count the number of kids in other cars you can see who are having a terrible time on long boring car journeys with their families.

9. Take a *Star Trek* matter-transporter machine with you, get beamed to your destination immediately, and surprise your parents by getting there before they do.

10. Eat your own left leg to stop yourself going mad with boredom.

THE VERY
SILLIEST
LISTS
OF ALL

Ten Lists We Weren't Allowed to Put in This Book

1. Ten Sure-fire Ways to Cheat in Tests and Not Get Found Out.

2. Ten Things Your Teacher Doesn't Want You to Know about Him/Her.

3. The Ten Steps to Total Control over Your Parents' Minds.

4. Ten Great, Fool-proof Classroom Hiding-places for Sweets.

5. Ten Ways of Hacking into Your Dad's Bank Account and Spending All His Money on Sweets, CDs, Trainers, Computer Games, etc.

6. Ten Ways of Getting Rid of Your Brother/Sister Permanently.

7. Ten Secrets That Will Make You Dictator of Planet Earth.

8. The Ten Most Utterly Disgusting Jokes Ever Told in a School Playground.

9. Ten Things That Go into School Dinners That They Didn't Want You to Know About.

10. Ten Mysterious Magical Signs on The Cover of This Book That Would Make You Want to Buy It as Soon as You Laid Eyes on It.

Ten Things That Would Happen If the World Were Properly Organized

1. Every day would be Christmas.
2. Teachers would be funny and interesting.
3. All children would have their own personal genie.
4. Fox hunting would be allowed, but the fox would be in a large, powerful, heavily armed tank, and it would be doing the hunting.
5. School dinners would be provided by any pizza or hamburger restaurant you might care to name.
6. Homework would be banned, and any teacher giving it would be executed.
7. The World Cup would be played every three months, and nobody would be allowed to win it except _____ (insert name of team).

8. Your brother or sister would be your willing slave.

9. Children would be paid huge sums of money to stay in bed, read comics, watch grown-up films on TV, and generally do exactly what they want all the time.

10. I would be made Dictator of the Entire Planet.

Ten Free Gifts You'd Like to Find in a Cereal Packet

1. A Golden Ticket.
2. A super-powerful ray gun that turns anything into chocolate.
3. A letter from the Prime Minister making you head of your school.
4. A TV the size of a large wall.
5. A cheque for one million pounds.
6. A magic spell that would enable you to silence your brother or sister by just clicking your fingers.
7. A pet rhinoceros.
8. A lifetime's free pass to every theme park in the world, plus a ticket for unlimited air travel there and back.
9. A secret scientific formula telling you how to make a potion that will give you super powers.
10. A small plastic model of a character from a crummy movie you don't want to see.

Ten Things That Don't Go Down Well in a Supermarket

1. Pretending the trolley is a Formula One racing car or, worse still, a tank.
2. Wearing a large rucksack and knocking over piles of tins every time you turn around.

3. Leaving the corpse of your dead hamster in one of the aisles, then shrieking, 'Eeek! There's a dead hamster on the floor!'

4. Playing cricket in one of the aisles with French bread for a bat, an orange for a ball, and a pile of tins for a wicket.

5. Talking in a loud voice about the vomiting, diarrhoea, etc, brought on by something you bought at this supermarket just the week before ...

6. Pulling that large plug out of the socket near the freezer cabinets.

7. Telling all the other customers that the other supermarket down the road is much better, and is giving away thousands-of-pounds-worth of free food that day.

8. Playing marbles on the floor near the check-outs when there are long queues.

9. Re-arranging all the packets on one of the shelves to spell your name.

10. Going back the week after you've done all this and doing it all over again.

Ten Things You Can't Imagine the Royal Family Doing

1. Eating chips out of the bag while watching *EastEnders*.
2. Forming a pop group, making a record and appearing on *Top of the Pops*.

3.   Giving each other a Chinese burn until one of them gives up.

4.   Becoming a synchronized swimming team and winning a gold medal at the next Olympics.

5.   Ordering a takeaway curry then arguing over who should pay for it.

6.   Deciding to have Mohican haircuts and their noses pierced.

7.   Playing hopscotch in the grounds of Buckingham Palace.

8.   Inviting the Prime Minister round for a game of hide-and-seek.

9.   The Queen and Princess Anne getting jobs as dinner ladies at your school.

10. Getting rid of the corgis and replacing them with pit bull terriers.

Ten Very Silly Ways
to Watch TV

1. Upside down, with your feet superglued to the ceiling.
2. Over your shoulder, through the wrong end of a telescope.

3. From inside a large cardboard box, with two very small holes cut out for your eyes.

4. With the sound turned right down and the contrast turned to totally black.

5. While wearing a Viking helmet, orange wellington boots, and singing some impressive operatic arias.

6. From another room, while you're trying to work out if you've got X-ray vision.

7. Inside a cage at the zoo, with a lion who hasn't been fed for a while ...

8. While trying to beat the world record for balancing chairs on the end of your nose.

9. With a granny who only ever watches gardening programmes and *Songs of Praise*.

10. With a brown paper bag over your head.

Ten Things You Don't Want to See Falling Out of Your Birthday Cards

1. 10p.
2. A large, angry, claustrophobic tarantula.

3. An I.O.U. from your mum and dad.
4. Your grandad's toe-nail clippings.
5. A voucher entitling you to a ten-per-cent discount off a school maths textbook of your choice.
6. A cheque from your granny made out to your brother or sister.
7. A token for £100, redeemable only at a shop called 'Clothes For Kiddies – Fashions for Juveniles with That Fabulous Fifties Feel'.
8. A ticket for a return trip to New York on *The Titanic Mark II*.
9. A voucher entitling you to £1000 worth of goodies from your favourite CD/computer/clothes store with the words, 'Not to Be Used after December 31st 1999' stamped all over it.
10. A hamster squashed flat in the post.

Ten Parts of Your Body You Never Think About

1. Your left elbow.
2. The seventh eyelash (counting from the right) on your left eye.
3. Your interior vena cava.
4. The bit between the second and third toes on your right foot.
5. Your spleen.
6. The areas behind your knees.
7. Your ninth vertebra (counting down from the top).
8. The fourth baby tooth you left under your pillow for The Tooth Fairy.
9. The one-centimetre-square area of skin in the middle of your left shoulder.
10. The top of your right ear.

Ten Names You Don't Hear Much Any More

1. Clovis.
2. Boniface.
3. Claribel.
4. Wilbert.
5. Vortigern.
6. Gertrude.
7. Horatio.
8. Prasutagus.
9. Cuthbert.
10. Athanasia.

Ten Slightly Unfamiliar Sayings

1. There's no smoke without ... well, a lot of bits of wispy stuff floating around in the air and smelling as if something's been burned.

2. Every cloud has ... an aeroplane in it.

3. Early to bed and early to rise ... means you miss all the late films on TV.

4. All work and no play ... makes Jack a completely unbelievable schoolboy.

5. A stitch in time saves ... you from having to finish that cross-country race.

6. A friend in need ... is probably someone you should avoid like the plague.

7. Too many cooks ... means that you must have wandered into a training centre for TV chefs, or something.

8. Money is the root of all evil ... but that's OK so long as I've got plenty.

9. The family that plays together ... usually ends up having a huge row.

10. He who laughs last, laughs longest ... unless you stuff an old sock in his mouth first.

Ten Things You Wouldn't Like to Find in Your Pocket

1. A small spaceship containing a large number of tiny, vicious alien monsters armed to the teeth with tiny, vicious alien weapons capable of inflicting enormous damage on you, who think your hand is a gigantic space-beast out to get them.

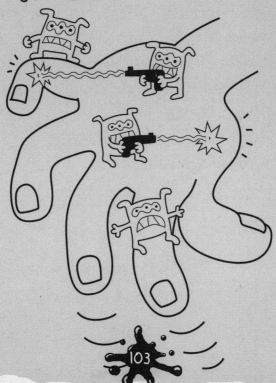

2. An extremely large, hairy, grumpy tarantula.

3. A mousetrap strong enough to break your fingers.

4. A cheque for a million pounds with the words 'Bank of Toyland' printed across the top of it.

5. A large amount of very runny, extremely smelly and wet dog poo.

6. A leaky canister of highly toxic radioactive waste.

7. Ten metres of rotting intestine from a dead yak.

8. A note from your mum and dad saying they've moved house, but without the new address on it.

9. A broken tube of superglue.

10. A dead hamster.

Ten
Totally
Uninteresting
Numbers

1. $9\frac{3}{4}$.
2. 217.
3. 4.
4. 3.
5. $1,276,841\frac{1}{2}$.
6. 87,962.
7. 9/16ths.
8. 3.169999, etc.
9. 408.
10. 1.76543.

Ten Things That Don't Go Down Too Well in the Waiting Room at Your Doctor's Surgery

1. Saying, 'I'm here to see the doctor about my bubonic plague' in a loud voice to the receptionist when you arrive.

2. Bringing your pet crocodile with you, especially if you haven't fed him for a few days.

3. Saying, 'I think I'm going to be sick' in a loud voice every five minutes.

4. Blowing your nose in spectacular fashion in a large hanky, examining what you've produced, then shaking the hanky around before putting it in your pocket.

5. Saying, 'I need to go to the toilet ... badly' in a loud voice several times.

6. Pestering everybody to play musical chairs and pass-the-parcel.
7. Saying, 'Is it true that Doctor _____'s nickname is ... the Butcher?' in a loud voice, at least once.
8. Arranging to play football there with your mates.
9. Saying, 'You know, the doctor down the road is much better' in a loud voice over and over again.
10. Whistling tunelessly.

Ten Very Silly Things to Wear on Your Head

1. A baby's potty.
2. The incredible hat your granny wore to your auntie's wedding, which blocked out one entire side of the family in the group photograph.
3. A detailed scale model of the *HMS Victory*, Nelson's flagship.
4. An empty dustbin.
5. Your underpants (although check that they're clean first).
6. A cageful of ferrets with bad stomachs.
7. A baseball cap with the words, 'I am an idiot' on the front.
8. A baseball cap with the words, 'Please hit me on the head with a large sledgehammer' on the back.
9. A huge bird's nest containing several very hungry vultures.
10. A thimble.

Ten Books You Thought You Might Have Read, But Probably Haven't

1. *Charlie and the Small Hydraulic Closed-Steel-Spring Factory* by Ronald Dahl.
2. *The Sheep-dog* by Rick Queen-Smythe.
3. *The Lion, the Witch and the Chest of Drawers* by C.T. Lewis.
4. *The Tale of Peter Hamster* by Beatrix Potty.
5. *Just Wilhelmina* by Richard Cramped-Leg.
6. *Swallows and Gulps* by Arthur Winsome.
7. *Winnie the Poo* by A.A. Roadside-Cleanup.
8. *Watership Up* by Adam Richards.
9. *The Lord of the Squares* by J.R.R. Talcum.
10. *Alice in Wolverhampton* by Carol Lewis.

Ten Very Silly Names for Imaginary Dinosaurs

1. Tyrannosaurus Eric.
2. Tricerabottoms.
3. Diplodocushocuspocus, The Magical Dinosaur.
4. Brian.
5. Hamstersaurus.
6. Terry O'Dactyl, The Irish Dinosaur.
7. Yo Cool Dude, The Hip-Hop Rappin' Raptor.
8. Iguanadonna, Queen of Dino-Pop.
9. Bore-o-saurus, The Very Dull Dinosaur.
10. Dilly.

Ten Excuses I Came up with to Get out of Writing This Book

1. 'I can't find my pen!'

2. 'No one will buy this stupid book anyway.'

3. 'My mum says I can't do it because I haven't tidied my room.'

4. 'There's something much more interesting on daytime TV.'

5. 'A giant alien spaceship has just landed in my garden, several small green aliens are getting out, and they're saying, "Urgh glob! Zing hoo-zhar kling-on Star Trek Darth Vader Hoot Vargon dee zed!"' (Translation: Don't write The Very Silly Lists book! It will endanger the future of the entire galaxy!)

6. 'I can't find the "on" switch for my computer.'

7. 'Book ... what book?'

111

8. 'Because of an injury to Michael Owen, I'll have to play for England in a vital World Cup qualifying match which just happens to be today.'

9. 'In reality, I am secret agent 008 and I'm going to be a bit busy over the next few months as I'll be engaged in a deadly struggle with a teacher who wants to become Dictator of the Entire Universe.'

10. 'I can't find my brain.'

Ten People Who Didn't Help Much in the Writing of This Book

1. Attila the Hun.
2. My great grandfather (he died in 1927).
3. Steven Spielberg.
4. That bloke who lives down the road, who says hello to me every time we bump into each other, and whose name I can never remember.
5. The President of the USA.
6. William Shakespeare.
7. My auntie Mavis (she was on holiday).
8. The Queen.
9. The manager of the England Football Team.
10. My editor – just joking, ha ha! *(Very funny – you're fired – The Editor.)*

Gerbil Crazy!

by Tony Bradman

'Mum, can I have a gerbil?'

Sarah's parents don't like the idea of a gerbil in the house.
And when Sarah's gerbil Georgie keeps escaping, they're
not very happy at all. They have to spend hours trying to
catch him!

Then one day Sarah asks if she can take Georgie to school.
But her mum isn't keen. 'You know what Georgie's like,'
she says. 'If he escapes at school, you might never find him
again.' But Sarah won't take no for an answer.

A warm and amusing story for all young children who
know what trouble – and fun – pets can be!

One Nil

by Tony Bradman

Dave Brown is football mad!

Dave dreams about it all the time. So when he finds out that the England squad are coming to train at his local club, he just *has* to go and watch them. But how can he? What about school? It seems impossible, but then Dave has a plan – a plan that leads him to scoring a goal of a lifetime.

Smile Please

by Tony Bradman

My name's Tracey
And I'm always
Bonk ... Owww!
Falling over.

Neil has the same problem with the wobbly wheel on his bike! Then there's Helen who can't stop bouncing and Sarah who can't stop skipping and Paul who likes kicking his football against the wall best ...

These are just a few of the people you can meet in Tony Bradman's first collection of poetry. There's plenty of fun on every page.

Tommy Niner and the Moon of Doom

by Tony Bradman

'Sounds like mission impossible to me, Tommy.'

Tommy Niner and his dad think they have an easy mission – to take the stroppy Admiral Kelvin back home to Galactic HQ. Instead they are hurled through space in search of the Admiral's runaway daughter. With Tommy in the driving seat, the spaceship lands in some seriously dodgy places, including the Moon of Doom …

Tommy Niner and the Mystery Spaceship

by Tony Bradman

When the crew of the Stardust narrowly miss an invisible
spaceship gone adrift, their troubles have only just begun.

Tommy and Grandad go on board to explore, and discover
Evil Zarella, the notorious space pirate, and her crew deep-
frozen. Then Grandad starts fiddling – and the temperature
begins to rise!

Space chases, lethal gas clouds and alien pot plants ensure
that Tommy is never out of the hot seat in this second
spectacular space adventure with Tommy Niner.

READ MORE IN PUFFIN

For children of all ages, Puffin represents quality and variety – the very best in publishing today around the world.

For complete information about books available from Puffin – and Penguin – and how to order them, contact us at the appropriate address below. Please note that for copyright reasons the selection of books varies from country to country.

On the World Wide Web: www.penguin.co.uk

In the United Kingdom: Please write to *Dept. EP, Penguin Books Ltd, Bath Road, Harmondsworth, West Drayton, Middlesex UB7 ODA*

In the United States: Please write to *Penguin Putnam inc., P.O. Box 12289, Dept B, Newark, New Jersey 07101-5289* or call 1-800-788-6262.

In Canada: Please write to *Penguin Books Canada Ltd, 10 Alcorn Avenue, Suite 300, Toronto, Ontario M4V 3B2*

In Australia: Please write to *Penguin Books Australia Ltd, P.O. Box 257, Ringwood, Victoria 3134*

In New Zealand: Please write to *Penguin Books (NZ) Ltd, Private Bag 102902, North Shore Mail Centre, Auckland 10*

In India: Please write to *Penguin Books India Pvt Ltd, 11 Panscheel Shopping Centre, Panscheel Park, New Delhi 110 017*

In the Netherlands: Please write to *Penguin Books Netherlands bv, Postbus 3507, NL-1001 AH Amsterdam*

In Germany: Please write to *Penguin Books Deutschland GmbH, Metzlerstrasse 26, 60594 Frankfurt am Main*

In Spain: Please write to *Penguin Books S. A., Bravo Murillo 19, 1° B, 28015 Madrid*

In Italy: Please write to *Penguin Italia s.r.l., Via Felice Casati 20, I–20124 Milano*

In France: Please write to *Penguin France S. A., 17 rue Lejeune, F–31000 Toulouse*

In Japan: Please write to *Penguin Books Japan, Ishikiribashi Building, 2–5–4, Suido, Bunkyo-ku, Tokyo 112*

In South Africa: Please write to *Longman Penguin Southern Africa (Pty) Ltd, Private Bag X08, Bertsham 2013*